first field guide
to australian

text **pat slater**

search &learn

Steve Parish
DISCOVER & LEARN
ABOUT AUSTRALIA

Contents

p. 33

MAMMALS

p. 20

2 p. 11

p. 45

p. 55

p. 25

Australia's mammals

A mammal is a warm-blooded, furry animal that feeds its young on milk. This guide describes some of Australia's native[G] mammals, such as kangaroos, possums, bandicoots and bats.

p. 25

PETER SLATER

Introduced[G] mammals were imported after 1788. Some, such as goats, pigs and rabbits, have run wild and compete with native mammals for food and water. Others, such as foxes and cats, eat native mammals.

Fox

Where to start?

Many Australian mammals are shy or rare, and most are active at night. Introduced mammals are often easier to spot in the wild. However, possums, bandicoots, flying-foxes, insectivorous bats, native rodents and antechinus may visit suburban backyards. Kangaroos and wallabies lose their fear of humans where they are protected, such as in national parks. Seals, whales and dolphins can be seen at the coast.

p. 24

How to see mammals

- Go to a zoo and visit the walk-through and night-time exhibits.
- Go to a national park or wildlife sanctuary.
- Walk through the bush. Look up in trees and under bushes. Sit quietly by a creek. Search for mammal tracks and droppings.
- Walk, ride a bicycle or travel by car along outer suburban roads at dawn.
- Go on a whale-watching, seal-watching or flying-fox-watching trip.
- Watch for dolphins at the beach.
- Put out suitable food for possums or bandicoots.
- Make contact with people who care for injured native animals (ask your State wildlife body for details).
- Watch for bats at dusk.
- Wherever you go, stay on full alert for flashes of fur.

What am I seeing?

Read books on animal behaviour to discover reasons why mammals act as they do.

When watching...

Make like a tree. Mammals have keen senses. When startled, they freeze, then escape. If you try to make yourself into part of the landscape, the animals will know you are there, but with luck they may ignore you.

☺ Some hints

Wear clothes that don't rustle or flap.
Move slowly and smoothly.
Approach in a zig-zag.
Stalk against the wind.
Freeze when the animal looks at you.
Keep moving when it relaxes.

☻ Some don'ts

Don't carry a stick or stone.
Don't talk loudly, or move suddenly.
Don't take your dog.
Don't expect to see mammals at midday. Try dawn, dusk and early night.

What mammal is it?

To help identify a mammal, note:

Size – relate size to well-known mammal, e.g. mouse, rat, cat, dog.

Shape – note head, neck, body, tail, legs.

Colour – name parts of the body as shown below.

Habitat[G] – where does the mammal feed and shelter? Is this natural or not?

Range[G] – is this mammal likely to be in this area?

Food – what is it eating?

Collect droppings[G] – if available, take to a museum in a plastic bag for identification.

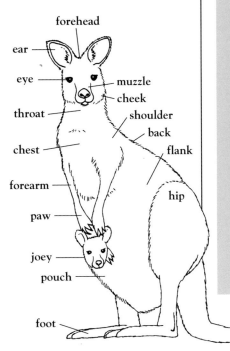

forehead
ear
eye
throat
chest
forearm
paw
joey
pouch
foot
muzzle
cheek
shoulder
back
flank
hip
tail

It is usually easy to identify a mammal as a member of a group, e.g. a wallaby, but difficult to tell just which species[G] it is. In the field, make notes and a drawing. Later, identify the animal from a reference book. First find the group the animal belongs to in the Index, then turn to the text and illustrations. Eliminate some species on range and habitat, then identify the animal on shape, colour and markings.

Naming mammals

A mammal is given:

1. An official common name
e.g. Common Wombat.

2. A scientific name
e.g. *Vombatus ursinus*.
This is used all over the world.
It is written in italics, and the
word order is reversed from the
order used in English. In this
Guide the scientific name is
followed by a translation
(*Vombatus ursinus* means
"bear-like wombat".)

3. Unofficial local names
e.g. Naked-nosed Wombat,
Forest Wombat.

p. 24

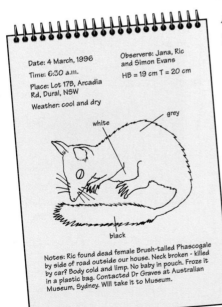

Date: 4 March, 1996
Time: 6:30 a.m.
Place: Lot 17B, Arcadia Rd, Dural, NSW
Weather: cool and dry

Observers: Jana, Ric and Simon Evans
HB = 19 cm T = 20 cm

white
grey
black

Notes: Ric found dead female Brush-tailed Phascogale by side of road outside our house. Neck broken - killed by car? Body cold and limp. No baby in pouch. Froze it in a plastic bag. Contacted Dr Graves at Australian Museum, Sydney. Will take it to Museum.

Abbreviations used in this book

HB = length of head + body
T = length of tail
HBT = head + body + tail
W = weight
♀ = female ♂ = male
Aust. = mainland Australia
Tas. = Tasmania only
NSW = New South Wales
WA = Western Australia
SA = South Australia
NT = Northern Territory
ᴳ = Glossary (p. 56)

Note: Where there is a great
size difference between female
and male of one species,
average measurements for
each sex are given.

Spot the mammal

There are three groups of mammals in Australia.

1) MONOTREMES, whose babies hatch from eggs, e.g. echidna.

Short-beaked Echidna, a monotreme

2) MARSUPIALS, whose newborn babies attach to their mothers' nipples to complete developing (sometimes in a pouch), e.g. wallaby.

Red-necked Wallabies are marsupials

3) PLACENTAL MAMMALS, whose babies are born well-developed, e.g. bat.

Black Flying-fox, a placental mammal

Nearly 20 species of Australian mammals have become extinct[G] in the past 200 years. At present, another 22 species are considered to be in danger of extinction.

STANLEY BREEDEN

Monotreme, marsupial or placental mammal?

MONOTREMES

PLATYPUS (p.10)   ECHIDNA (p.11)

MARSUPIALS

PHASCOGALE (p.12)

DUNNART (p.14)

QUOLL (p.16)

THYLACINE (p.18)

MARSUPIAL MOLE (p.19)

NUMBAT (p.20)

BILBY (p.21)

BANDICOOT (p.22)

KOALA (p.23)

WOMBAT (p.24)

BRUSHTAIL POSSUM (p.25)

COMMON RINGTAIL (p.27)

PYGMY-POSSUM (p.28)

SUGAR GLIDER (p.30)

HONEY-POSSUM (p.33)

PADEMELON (p.36)

QUOKKA (p.37)

ROCK-WALLABY (p.38)

WALLABY (p.39-41)

TREE-KANGAROO (p.42)

GREY KANGAROO (p.43)

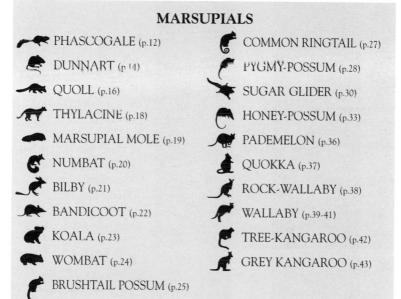

PLACENTAL MAMMALS

FLYING-FOX (p.46)

BAT (p.47)

BUSH-RAT (p.48)

HOPPING-MOUSE (p.49)

SEA-LION (p.51)

DOLPHIN (p.52)

WHALE (p.54)

DUGONG (p.53)

DINGO (p.55)

🐾 Platypus

Ornithorhynchus anatinus (= duck-like bird-bill)

PETER MARSACK

Where found: In or near fresh water along east coast Aust.; Tas.

Habits: Active at dawn and dusk. Catches small animals underwater, stores them in cheek pouches, surfaces to eat. Digs rest burrows in river bank. Female lays two rubbery eggs, 17 mm in diameter, in nest burrow, incubates[G] 2 weeks. Feeds young on milk from patches on her belly for 4–5 months.

Length: HBT: ♀ 40 ♂ 55 cm

Weight: ♀ 700 ♂ 2000 g

Identification: Cat-sized, freshwater mammal with smooth, brown fur. Has leathery bill, no visible ears, flattened body, broad tail, webbed feet. Swimming, makes a V-shaped bow-wave.

Notes: Male can inject venom[G] through spurs on ankles. Baby has milk teeth, but loses them at weaning[G].

Status: Vulnerable. Disappears when habitat altered.

Similar species: Water Rat has visible ears and "dog-paddles" when swimming.

HABITAT CREEKS & RIVERS

FOOD WATER ANIMALS

Short-beaked Echidna

Tachyglossus aculeatus (= spiny fast-tongue)

Length: HB 30–45 cm

Weight: 2–7 kg

Identification: Cat-sized, spine-covered, long-snouted ground animal, with powerful claws and tiny tail.

Where found: Aust. and Tas.

Habits: Active at night and on dull winter days. Claws into ant and termite nests, pulls out insects with sticky tongue. Female lays one egg, incubates it for 10 days in her pouch, suckles young for 12 weeks (in pouch, then in burrow).

Notes: Male has spurs, but no venom. Digs into ground or wedges into hollow when threatened. "Trains" of several males follow one female, hoping to mate with her. Droppings contain soil.

Status: Secure. Common.

Similar species: None.

HABITAT
NEAR FOOD
SOURCES

FOOD
ANTS &
TERMITES

Brush-tailed Phascogale

Phascogale tapoatafa (= pouched-weasel called by Aborigines *tapoatafa*)

Length: HB ♀ 180 ♂ 200 cm; T ♀ 19 ♂ 21 cm

Weight: ♀ 160 ♂ 230 g

Identification: Large-rat-sized tree-dweller, with soft grey body fur, long bushy black tail. Runs up and down trunks, on and under branches, can leap up to 2 m between trees.

Where found: Open coastal forest around Aust.

Habits: Spends day in tree hollow, at night hunts insects and small mammals. May eat nectar. Female carries 3–8 young on nipples for 7 weeks, then leaves and feeds them in nest for 13 weeks.

Notes: Can rotate hindfoot 180° to climb up or down. Alarmed, taps forefeet on branch. All males die after mating (from stress-related illnesses, or are taken by predators). Females survive to give birth to new generation.

Status: Rare. Threatened by habitat destruction, cats, foxes.

Similar species: Endangered, rare Red-tailed Phascogale has upper part of tail rust-red.

HABITAT
COASTAL
FORESTS

FOOD
INSECTS &
SMALL LIFE

Yellow-footed Antechinus

Antechinus flavipes (= yellow-footed hedgehog-like* animal)

Length: HB ♀ 10.5 ♂ 12 cm;
T ♀ 8.5 ♂ 10 cm

Weight: ♀ 3.5 ♂ 5.6 g

Identification: Looks like large mouse with big ears, longish snout. Has grey head, light rings around eyes, reddish rump, belly and sides, yellow-brown feet. Black tail tip.

Where found: Many habitats, including gardens, from north-eastern Qld to southwestern WA.

Habits: Spends day in nest under log or leaves. At night hunts insects, house mice, other small animals. Moves in quick rushes, searches leaf litter, climbs.

Notes: May enter houses looking for mice and spiders. In spring, males mate (act may last up to 12 hours) then die. Females carry up to 10 young for 5 weeks, then suckle them in nest for 15 weeks.

Status: Secure. Common. Often caught by cats.

Similar species: Brown Antechinus is grey-brown above, paler below, lacks light eye-rings.

* Damp antechinus fur looks spiky.

HABITAT
WOODED
AREAS

FOOD
INSECTS &
SMALL LIFE

Fat-tailed Dunnart

Sminthopsis crassicaudata (= fat-tailed mouse-like animal)

Length: HB 6–9 cm; T 4–7cm

Weight: 10–20 g

Identification: Large-mouse-sized, grey-brown hunter with large ears, fat tail. Large eyes in dark eye-rings, very pointed muzzle, long, narrow hindfeet.

Where found: Woodlands, plains, farmlands across southern and central Aust.

Habits: Shelters during day in nest in hole, or under log. Hunts at night for insects and other small animals. Usually 5 young, carried in well-developed pouch for 5 weeks, fed in nest for 5 weeks.

Notes: Several may share nest in cold weather. Fat in tail is winter food reserve. May have increased range with clearing of land.

Status: Secure. Common.

Similar species: Stripe-faced Dunnart is a fat-tailed, inland species with dark facial stripe.

HABITAT
WOODLANDS
& PLAINS

FOOD
INSECTS &
SMALL LIFE

Kultarr

Antechinomys laniger (= woolly-furred mouse-like animal)

Length: HB 8.5 cm;
T 12–13 cm

Weight: 20–30 g

Identification:
Large-mouse-sized, large-eared hunter with long hindlegs, long, tuft ended tail. Brown-grey above, white below. Bounds rather than hops.

Where found: Desert inland plains, stony and sandy land.

Habits: Shelters during day in a burrow. Hunts at night for insects, spiders and other small animals. 6–8 young carried by female, protected by fold of skin on belly, for 4 weeks, then left in nest for 9 weeks. Later ride on mother's back while she hunts. Weaned at 12 weeks.

Notes: An active desert predator.

M & I MORCOMBE

Status: Probably secure. Vulnerable to habitat changes.

Similar species: None.

HABITAT
INLAND
DESERT

FOOD
INSECTS &
SMALL LIFE

Spotted-tailed Quoll

Dasyurus maculatus (= spotted hairy-tailed animal)

IAN MORRIS

Length: HB small ♀ 35 large ♂ 76 cm; T ♀ 34 ♂ 55 cm

Weight: ♀ to 4 kg, ♂ to 7 kg

Identification: Small-dog-sized hunter with brown, white-spotted body and long, spotted tail. Bounds on ground, climbs trees.

Where found: In isolated forest areas down east coast of Aust., and in Tas.

Habits: Prey ranges from insects to small wallabies, also carrion[G]. Droppings made in special places in territory. Mating lasts up to 8 hours. Female develops pouch, 5 young remain there for 7 weeks, fed in nest 6 weeks.

Notes: Largest marsupial predator[G] on mainland. Male feeds female and young.

Status: Disappearing through habitat destruction, competition with fox, cat.

Similar species: Northern and Eastern Quolls unspotted tails; Eastern Quoll only rarely recorded on mainland.

HABITAT
FOREST, WOODLAND

FOOD
LIVE ANIMALS, CARRION

16

Tasmanian Devil

Sarcophilus harrisii (= Harris's flesh-eater)

Length: HB ♀ 57 ♂ 65 cm; T ♀ 24 ♂ 26 cm

Weight: ♀ 7 ♂ 9 kg

Identification: Black scavenger with white markings on chest and rump. Looks like a medium-sized, bulky dog.

Where found: All over Tas., especially in northeast.

Habits: Spends day in den. Dusk to dawn hunts for dead animals, insects, small mammals. Can climb trees. 2–4 young born April, carried in rear-opening pouch for 16 weeks, then left in den. Young on own at 40 weeks.

Notes: Largest living marsupial carnivore[G]. Lived on mainland until around 400 years ago. Group feeding at carcass may squabble loudly. Not dangerous to humans or their animals.

Status: Secure, common in Tas.

Similar species: None.

HABITAT ALL OVER TASMANIA

FOOD LIVE ANIMALS, CARRION

17

 # Thylacine

Thylacinus cynocephalus (= dog-headed pouched dog)

Length: HB 100–130 cm; T 50–65 cm

Weight: 15–35 kg

Identification: Doglike (kelpie to greyhound-sized), with large head, stripes on upper surface, thick-based tail.

Where found: Tas. until 1933. Last captive animal died 1936.

Habits: Chased down kangaroos, wallabies and small animals. After European settlement, killed sheep and was ruthlessly hunted.

The 2–3 young were reared in a rear-opening pouch. Larger young were left in den until able to hunt with their mother.

Notes: Became extinct on the mainland 2000 or less years ago (displaced by the Dingo, a more efficient predator). Probably extinct in Tasmania by the 1930s. Possibly only a few thousand existed in Tasmania at any time.

Status: Thought to be extinct.

Similar species: None.

PAUL BYRNE

HABITAT WAS TASMANIA

FOOD WALLABIES & SMALL ANIMALS

Marsupial Mole

Notoryctes typhlops (= blind southern digger)

STANLEY BREEDEN

Length: HB 12–16 cm; T 2 cm

Weight: 40–70 g

Identification: Rat-sized, burrowing marsupial with golden, silky fur. Blind. Horny shield on nose; no visible ears. 2 bladelike front claws are used for digging and gripping prey.

Where found: Sandy deserts from central Aust. to north-west coast of WA.

Habits: The Marsupial Mole lives in sand, digging tunnels which collapse behind it. Eats insects found underground; may surface after rain. Female has rear-opening pouch and two nipples.

Notes: Little known. Adapted to life underground, the Marsupial Mole looks very like the true moles, which are unrelated placental mammals.

Status: Not known. It is very rarely seen.

Similar species: None.

 HABITAT SANDY DESERTS

 **FOOD** BURROWING ANIMALS

Numbat

Myrmecobius fasciatus (= striped ant-eater)

M & I MORCOMBE

Length: HB 24 cm; T 17 cm

Weight: 460–484 g

Identification: Cat-sized, red-brown marsupial with dark rump striped with white. Narrow head, sharp muzzle, dark stripe through eye. Long tail "bottle-brushes" when the owner is active.

Where found: Survives in a few isolated eucalypt forests in southwestern WA.

Habits: Active during day. Shelters and sleeps in a hollow fallen log. May dig a burrow. Feeds on termites, scratched and licked with long, slender tongue from under rotting wood or surface tunnels.

Notes: Once found across southern Australia from western NSW to coast of WA. 4 young born January, carried for 5 months, then fed in nest 5 months.

Status: Rare and endangered. Threatened by habitat loss, foxes, fires.

Similar species: None.

HABITAT
EUCALYPT
FORESTS

FOOD
TERMITES

Greater Bilby

Macrotis lagotis (= hare-eared large-eared animal)

Length: HB ♀ 34 ♂ 42 cm; T ♀ 24 ♂ 25 cm

Weight: ♀ 950 ♂ 1750 g

Identification: Small-cat-sized burrowing marsupial with long ears, long muzzle, soft grey fur. Long, black, white-tipped tail.

Where found: Desert areas of central Aust. with little free surface water.

Habits: Shelters during day in a burrow that may be 3 m long and nearly 2 m deep. Gets moisture from insects, seeds, fungi; digs feeding holes 10 cm deep. Droppings may contain sand. 2 young stay in the rear-opening pouch for about 11 weeks, then are left in burrow.

Notes: Once found in dry areas across southern Australia. Threatened by grazing, fire, rabbits and foxes.

Status: Rare and endangered.

Similar species: The Lesser Bilby is much smaller. It is almost certainly extinct.

HABITAT SANDY DESERTS

FOOD INSECTS & SEEDS

Isoodon obesulus (= equal-toothed* rather fat animal)

Length: HB ♀ 30 ♂ 33 cm; T ♀ 11 ♂ 12 cm

Weight: ♀ 700 ♂ 850 g

Identification: Cat-sized, ground-living bandicoot with pointed muzzle, humped back, thin tail. Grey-brown above and white below. Bounds and gallops when moving fast.

Where found: Across southwestern and southeastern Aust. and in Tas., in areas with sandy soil and low ground cover. Increases after low-level fires renew vegetation.

Habits: Solitary[6]. Shelters in nest on ground during day, feeds on insects, earthworms and fungi at night, leaving conical holes in ground. Up to six young are carried in a rear-opening pouch, then weaned at around 9 weeks.

Notes: Needs home range of up to 7 hectares to supply food needs. Individuals' ranges may overlap if food plentiful.

Status: Becoming less common as its habitat disappears.

Similar species: The Long-nosed Bandicoot, found in the eastern part of this species' range, has longer, pointed muzzle, much larger ears and white feet.

* Refers to the length of the incisor teeth.

JIRI LOCHMAN

HABITAT HEATH & SCRUB

FOOD FUNGI & SMALL LIFE

Koala

Phascolarctos cinereus (= ash-coloured pouched bear)

Length: HB ♀ 69 ♂ 78 cm

Weight: ♀ 5 ♂ 12 kg

Identification: Medium-dog-sized, tree-living marsupial. Has big-bellied body, round face, round furry ears, flattened nose and strong limbs. Fur is grey-brown and woolly.

Where found: In remaining eucalypt forest in eastern Aust.

Habits: Night-active and solitary. Usually seen in eucalypt trees. The low energy content of its eucalypt leaf diet means a Koala sleeps up to 20 hours out of every 24. Female carries 1 young in rear-opening pouch for 6 months, then on her back for a further 6 months.

Notes: Southern Koalas are larger than northern ones. Once hunted for fur (to extinction in some areas). Vulnerable[G] to dogs when changing trees at night. Also threatened by disease and by bushfires.

Status: Probably secure. Common in suitable forest, but disappears with habitat.

Similar species: None.

HABITAT EUCALYPT FORESTS

FOOD EUCALYPT LEAVES

Common Wombat

Vombatus ursinus (= bear-like wombat)

Length: HB 90–115 cm; T 25 mm

Weight: 22–39 kg

Identification: Size of a large, stocky dog. A ground-living burrower, with a rounded outline, large head, naked nose and short ears. Grey to brown, coarse fur.

Where found: Coastal ranges, forest and woodland from northeastern NSW to southeastern SA.

Habits: Night-active and solitary. Several burrows will be dug in an area. Eats native grasses, shrubs, roots. In winter, may bask[G] or feed in daytime. Female carries one young in her rear-opening pouch for 6 months; it follows her for another 11 months.

Notes: Not protected in some areas of eastern Victoria. Large, rectangular droppings are left on logs and rocks. Major burrows may be up to 20 m long, with several chambers and entrances.

Status: Probably secure, but range decreasing.

Similar species: Northern and Southern Hairy-nosed Wombats are very rare. They have softer fur and hairy noses.

HABITAT WOODLANDS & FORESTS

FOOD GRASSES & SHRUBS

Common Brushtail Possum

Trichosurus vulpecula (= little fox-like hairy-tail)

Length: HB 35–55 cm; T 24–40 cm

Weight: ♀ 2.4 ♂ 2.9 kg

Identification: Cat-sized tree-living possum with foxy face, long oval ears and copper-coloured to grey fur. Bushy tail has a short naked area underneath. Agile climber, which sits upright and holds food in its paws.

Where found: All over Aust., in many habitats.

Habits: Spends day in hollow tree, cave or roof of building. At night eats leaves, flowers, fruit. Male marks territory with chin, chest and anal[G] glands. Breeds autumn and spring. Female carries one young for 4–5 months in pouch, then for 2 months on back. Coughing, hissing calls.

Notes: Once hunted for fur. Queensland has a short-haired copper form, Tasmania a larger, woolly, dark grey form.

Status: Secure. Common in forests and towns.

Similar species: Mountain Brushtail Possum has short rounded ears; tail has long naked area underneath.

HABITAT
FORESTS
& TOWNS

FOOD
LEAVES, FRUIT,
FLOWERS

Spotted Cuscus

Spilocuscus maculatus (= spotted spotted-cuscus)

Length: HB 35–58 cm; T 31–43 cm

Weight: 1.5–5 kg

Identification: Large-cat-sized, usually slow-moving tree-dweller. Round, bare-skinned face which may flush reddish, large round eyes, tiny ears. The prehensile⁶ tail is two-thirds naked underneath. Male is blotched grey and white above, female is grey.

Where found: Rainforests of Cape York Peninsula, north of Coen, Qld.

Habits: Spends day sleeping on branch or in leaves. At night, eats leaves, fruits, flowers. Large canine⁶ teeth suggest some animal food. Males may be aggressive towards each other. Usually 1 young, carried in mother's pouch, then on her back.

Notes: Can travel across bare ground to reach rainforest fragments. May make sleeping platform of leaves and twigs.

Status: Vulnerable. Needs suitable habitat for survival.

Similar species: Southern Common Cuscus is more possum-like, with longer snout, larger ears and stripe on back.

HABITAT N.E. QLD RAINFOREST

FOOD LEAVES & FLOWERS

Common Ringtail Possum

Pseudocheirus peregrinus (= wandering false-hand*)

Length: HB 30–35 cm; T 30–35 cm

Weight: 700–1100 g

Identification: Small-cat-sized possum. Each short ear has a white patch behind it. The long, prehensile, white-tipped tail, with a naked area beneath, is used as a fifth limb. Colour varies from copper to grey. Makes a soft, high, twittering call.

Where found: Down east coast from Cape York Peninsula to Tas., in areas with trees and shrubs; in gardens.

Habits: Spends day in a ball-shaped, leaf-lined nest in hollow or dense foliage. At night eats leaves and flowers. Male and female stay together for breeding season. 2 young are carried in the female's pouch for 4 months, then left in nest 2 months. Both parents care for the young.

Notes: Can digest eucalypt leaves. Soft droppings are produced in nest during day, eaten and extra nourishment extracted. Fond of rosebuds.

Status: Secure. Common in suitable habitat.

Similar species: Western Ringtail Possum, found only in southwestern WA, is considered rare, endangered.

* The tail serves as another hand.

HABITAT FORESTS & TOWNS

FOOD LEAVES & FLOWERS

Eastern Pygmy-possum

Cercartetus nanus (= dwarf cercartetus*)

Habits: Solitary. Spends day in hollow. At night eats pollen, nectar (gathered with brush-tipped tongue), fruits and insects. Female carries 4 young in her pouch for 4 weeks, then feeds them in a bark nest for 5 weeks.

Length: HB 7–11 cm; T 7.5–10.5 cm

Weight: 15–43 g

Identification: Mouse-sized possum with fat-based, prehensile tail. Fawn above, white below.

Where found: Down eastern coast from southern Qld to eastern SA, including Tas., in rainforest, eucalypts and heaths.

Notes: Becomes torpid[G] in cold weather, using up fat stored in the base of the tail.

Status: Secure. Common, but seldom seen.

Similar species: Little Pygmy-possum, mainly in Tas., is smaller, with grey belly. Western Pygmy-possum found in southeastern SA and southwestern WA.

* The meaning of this is unknown.

HABITAT
FOREST &
HEATHLAND

FOOD
NECTAR &
INSECTS

Leadbeater's Possum

Gymnobelideus leadbeateri (= Leadbeater's naked* glider)

Length: HB 15–17 cm; T 14.5–18 cm

Weight: 100 (spring)–166 (autumn) g

Identification: Shy, rat-sized possum, grey to brown above with dark stripe from face down back. Long tail broadens at tip. Active leaper.

Where found: Only in mountain forests of Vic.'s central highlands.

Habits: Active at night. Lives in colonies of up to 8, consisting of a breeding pair and offspring, which nest together in tree hollow. Feeds on insects, spiders found beneath bark, and tree sap. Female carries 1–2 young in her pouch for over 3 months. They leave the nest at 4 months of age.

Notes: Group membership signalled by scent. Group defends territory of up to 2 ha, will mob predator attacking colony member. This species was not sighted 1909–1961.

Status: Endangered. 75% of its habitat is in timber-production forests and only 3% in nature reserves. (Suitable nest holes are only found in trees over 120 years old.)

Similar species: Sugar Glider has gliding membranes⁶, and its tail does not broaden.

* Refers to lack of gliding membranes.

HABITAT MOUNTAIN FORESTS

FOOD SMALL LIFE, TREE SAP

Sugar Glider

Petaurus breviceps (= short-headed rope-dancer)

Length: HB 16–21 cm;
T 16.5–21 cm

Weight: ♀ 95 ♂ 160 g

Identification: Rat-sized glider, blue-grey to brown-grey above with dark stripe from forehead to middle of back; pale below. The membrane stretching from the fifth finger to the first toe on each side of the body is used to glide between trees.

Where found: In coastal forests and patches of woodland from Kimberley, WA, across north, then down to southeastern SA and Tas.

Habits: Active at night. Lives in colonies of up to 7 adults and their young in tree hollows. Feeds on tree sap, nectar, pollen, insects. Female carries 2 young in pouch for 2–3 months. They leave the nest aged 4-5 months.

Notes: Group recognises members by scent. In cold weather, group huddles and may become torpid. At 7–10 months, young leave their group to find new ranges. May live in garden nest boxes.

Status: Secure. Common in suitable open forests.

Similar species: Leadbeater's Possum lives in limited habitat and lacks membranes.

HABITAT
COASTAL
FORESTS

FOOD
SAP, NECTAR,
INSECTS

Feathertail Glider

Acrobates pygmaeus (= pygmy acrobat)

Length: HB 6.5–8 cm; T 7–8 cm

Weight: 10–14 g

Identification: Mouse-sized glider. Long tail has fringe of hair on either side. Gliding membranes between elbows and knees. Grey above, white below.

Where found: Forests and woodlands of eastern Aust.

Habits: Active at night. Feeds on nectar with brush-tipped tongue, also on pollen and insects. Groups feed and nest together in tree hollows. 3–4 young carried in pouch for 9 weeks, fed in nest for 5 weeks. Female may carry reserve embryos[6], which develop once larger young have been weaned.

Notes: World's smallest gliding mammal. Pads under toes, sharp claws and prehensile tail aid climbing.

Status: Probably secure. Found in disappearing old forests.

Similar species: None. The only small tree-dweller with a feather-like tail.

HABITAT
EASTERN
WOODLANDS

FOOD
NECTAR,
INSECTS

Striped Possum

Dactylopsila trivirgata (= three-striped naked-finger)

Length: HB 25–27 cm; T 31–34 cm

Weight: 250–530 g

Identification: Small-cat-sized, slender, black and white striped possum with long, slender fourth finger. It has a strong, sweet odour.

Where found: Rainforests and woodlands from Iron Range south to Townsville, Qld.

Habits: Active at night. It is a fast, agile climber, which leaps boldly between trees. Uses its sharp teeth to pull away bark, then pokes grubs or other insects out with its tongue, or hooks them out with its long fourth finger. Sleeps during day in a hollow lined with leaves. The female has 2 young.

Notes: Noisy when searching for food. Fighting or mating animals shriek and gurgle.

Status: Probably secure. Its limited habitat needs protection.

Similar species: No other tree-dwelling mammal has bold stripes.

HABITAT
RAINFOREST,
NORTH QLD

FOOD
INSECTS &
SMALL LIFE

Honey-possum

Tarsipes rostratus (= long-nosed tarsier*-foot)

Length: HB 4–9.4 cm;
T 4.5–11 cm

Weight: 7–12 g

Identification: Mouse-sized, long-snouted marsupial with long prehensile tail. Eyes on top of head. Fingers and toes have broad tips and nails, not claws. Grey-brown above, with darker stripe down back.

Where found: Coastal heaths of southwestern WA.

Habits: Feeds on nectar and pollen, using long, brush-tipped tongue. Sleeps during the day in an old bird nest or hollow grasstree stem. Becomes torpid in cold weather. 2–3 young carried in pouch for 2 months, fed in nest for 2 weeks. Embryos in reserve in female's body may develop after young have been weaned.

Notes: Has fewer teeth than other marsupials. Depends on banksias, grevilleas, etc., for food. Acts as pollinator.

M & I MORCOMBE

Status: Survives where habitat is preserved.

Similar species: The Western Pygmy-possum has a much shorter muzzle, shorter, fatter tail, larger ears and softer fur.

* Tarsiers, like humans, have nails rather than claws.

HABITAT
COASTAL
HEATH, WA

FOOD
NECTAR
& POLLEN

Musky Rat-kangaroo

Hypsiprymnodon moschatus (= musky* animal with teeth like a potoroo)

STANLEY BREEDEN

Length: HB 23 cm; T ♀ 14 cm

Weight: ♀ 510 ♂ 530 g

Identification: Large-rat-sized marsupial with long scaly tail. Only kangaroo relative to have 5 toes. Sits up, holds food in paws. Moves in bounds. Grey head, brown body.

Where found: Rainforests of North Qld.

Habits: Generally solitary. Feeds in morning and late afternoon on seeds, nuts, fungi and insects. Sleeps at night in a nest on the forest floor. 2 young are carried in the pouch for 5 months, then fed in a nest.

Notes: Smallest of the kangaroo group, but it is like a possum in having a "big toe", a simple stomach (so it cannot digest grass) and in birthing twins. It hides seeds in the leaf litter, then eats them later.

Status: Probably secure. Needs rainforest areas for survival.

Similar species: None.

* Musk is a strong animal scent.

HABITAT
RAINFOREST,
NORTH QLD

FOOD
SEEDS &
INSECTS

Long-nosed (Gilbert's) Potoroo

Potorous tridactylus (= three-toed potoroo)

Length: HB ♀ 34 ♂ 38 cm; T 23 cm

Weight: ♀ 1020 ♂ 1180 g

Identification: Fat-cat-sized marsupial with short feet and grasping paws. Bare skin stretches from its nose up a long snout. Moves like a little kangaroo. Grey-brown fur.

Where found: Scattered forests and heaths with thick ground cover and sandy soils, in coastal southeastern Aust. and Tas. One recent record in southwestern WA.

Habits: Feeds from dusk, digging small holes for roots, fungi and insects. Stays in or near cover. One young, carried in the pouch for 4 months.

Notes: Described by Governor Phillip in 1789. It has disappeared as its habitat has been cleared. Not seen in WA for over 100 years until rediscovered at Two Peoples Bay in 1994.

Status: Probably secure, in disappearing suitable habitat.

Similar species: Endangered Long-footed Potoroo, found in small areas in northeastern Vic. and southeastern NSW, is larger and has longer hindfeet.

JIRI LOCHMAN

 **HABITAT** FORESTS & HEATHS

FOOD ROOTS & FUNGI

Red-legged Pademelon

Thylogale stigmatica (= pouched-weasel with tattoos*)

Length: HB ♀ 46 ♂ 49 cm; T ♀ 36 ♂ 44 cm

Weight: ♀ 4 ♂ 5 kg

Identification: Small-dog-sized, stocky wallaby with short, stiff tail. Grey-brown above, cream below, with reddish cheeks, arms, hindlegs.

Where found: Coastal eastern Aust., from Cape York to Sydney, NSW, in dense eucalypt forest and in rainforest.

Habits: Feeds on leaves and fallen fruits in forest during day, grass on edges at night. Rarely grazes more than 70 m from forest edge, moving rapidly along runways.

Notes: Rests with tail forward under body. Warning alarm thump made with hindfeet. Joey^G carried in pouch for 28 weeks, weaned 9 weeks later.

Status: Secure in limited habitat.

Similar species: Red-necked Pademelon has reddish fur on neck, but not on hindlegs.

* This refers to faint dotted markings on neck and hip.

HABITAT FOREST, RAINFOREST

FOOD LEAVES & GRASS

Quokka

Setonix brachyurus (= bristle-footed short-tail)

Length: HB ♀ 47 ♂ 49 cm; T ♀ 26.5 ♂ 29 cm

Weight: ♀ 2.9 ♂ 3.6 kg

Identification: Large-cat-sized, hopping marsupial with short ears, short, stiff tail.

Where found: On Rottnest Is., off WA, and in wetter parts of southwestern WA.

Habits: Eats leaves rather than grass. Rottnest Is. has drought in summer and local Quokkas are helped by human feeding. One joey stays in the pouch about 5 months and is weaned 2 months later. A female may carry an embryo, which continues development after her joey is weaned.

Notes: Once common on southwestern mainland. Second Australian marsupial to be noted by European (Willem de Vlamingh, in 1696, thought it was a big rat).

Status: Vulnerable. Rarely seen on mainland.

Similar species: On mainland, rare Brush-tailed Bettong is larger and yellowish grey. It has a longer tail with a black crest of hair.

HABITAT
HEATHS & FORESTS

FOOD
LEAVES & HERBS

Yellow-footed Rock-wallaby

Petrogale xanthopus (= yellow-footed rock-weasel)

Length: HB 48–65 cm; T 57–70 cm

Weight: 6–11 kg

Identification: A colourful wallaby which hops across rocks. Grey-fawn above, white below, white stripe on cheek, side and hip. Ears, arms, hindlegs and feet are orange to yellow, tail is ringed with orange and dark brown.

Where found: Flinders Ranges, SA; Adavale Basin, Qld.

Habits: Active at night during summer, during day and night in winter. Lives in colonies of up to 100 in dry, rocky country, sometimes near water. Eats grass and leaves. Young in pouch for 6–7 months.

Notes: Has disappeared from former range since European settlement. Once it was heavily hunted for its skin. Today, it has to compete with feral goats and rabbits for food and drought may kill off 60% of the animals in an area.

Status: Vulnerable, though common in limited habitat.

Similar species: None.

HABITAT ROCKY COUNTRY

FOOD GRASS & LEAVES

Red-necked (Bennett's*) Wallaby

Macropus rufogriseus (= red-grey great-foot)

Length: HB ♀ 77 ♂ 82 cm;
T ♀ 72 ♂ 80 cm

Weight: ♀ 14 ♂ 19 kg

Identification: A medium-sized wallaby, grey to reddish above, with reddish-brown neck. Pale grey below. Black muzzle, paws and largest toe. White stripe on upper lip.

Where found: Eucalypt forests of southeastern Aust. and Tas. Grazes in open grassy areas bordering forest.

Habits: Solitary, but may graze in groups. Spends day in forest, feeds from late afternoon. Eats grasses and leaves.

Notes: Group splits into single animals when disturbed. Protected, but may be killed in open seasons in Qld and Tas. Joey carried in pouch for 40 weeks, then suckled for another 5–7 months. Reserve embryo stored in female develops and is born after joey leaves pouch.

Status: Secure. Common.

Similar species: Black-striped Wallaby in Qld and northern NSW has dark stripe down back and white stripe on hip.

* Name of the species in Tasmania.

 HABITAT EUCALYPT FORESTS

 **FOOD** GRASS & LEAVES

Pretty-face Wallaby

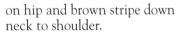

Macropus parryi (= Parry's great-foot)

Length: HB ♀ up to 75.5 ♂ up to 92 cm; T 78–94 cm

Weight: 11–16 kg

Identification: Medium-sized wallaby with long, slender tail, grey or brownish-grey above, white below. Dark brown forehead, base of ears. White stripe on upper lip, white stripe on hip and brown stripe down neck to shoulder.

Where found: Coastal eastern Aust. from Cooktown, Qld, to northern NSW, in areas with trees and grass.

Habits: Feeds during day on grass. Lives in groups of up to 50, each made up of smaller groups of 10 or less. Dominant[G] male mates with female. Joey carried in pouch for 37 weeks, then suckled another 9 months. Reserve embryo develops when pouch vacant.

Notes: When alarmed, thumps ground with hindfeet.

Status: Secure. Common.

Similar species: Black-striped Wallaby has dark back stripe.

HABITAT WOODLAND, FOREST

FOOD GRASSES

Agile Wallaby

Macropus agilis (= agile great-foot)

IAN MORRIS

Length: HB ♀ 65 ♂ 80 cm; T ♀ 74 ♂ 77 cm

Weight: ♀ 11 ♂ 19 kg

Identification: Large wallaby, brown above, whitish below. Light stripe on thigh, dark stripe up forehead, pale stripe on cheek. Hops with body almost upright, tail held straight out behind.

Where found: Grasslands across northern Aust. and down northeastern Qld coast.

Habits: Eats native grasses. Lives in groups of up to 10 which may become large mobs at feeding areas. Wary, easily alarmed. Joey stays in pouch 7–8 months, follows female until 12 months. Reserve embryo develops when pouch vacant.

Notes: Males much larger than females.

Status: Secure. Common.

Similar species: Several, but all far less common.

HABITAT
GRASS
LANDS

FOOD
NATIVE
GRASSES

Lumholtz's Tree-kangaroo

Dendrolagus lumholtzi (= Lumholtz's tree-hare)

STANLEY BREEDEN

Length: HB ♀ 55 ♂ 59 cm; T 70 cm

Weight: 6–7.5 kg

Identification: Medium-sized tree-climbing kangaroo with long, non-prehensile tail, strong front and hind limbs. Brownish-black in colour, with lighter fur on lower back. Pale brown band across forehead and down each side of face.

Where found: In highland rainforest in a very limited area of northeastern Qld.

Habits: Solitary. Spends day asleep, crouched in treetop. Eats leaves and fruit, holding them in paws. Joey stays in pouch for around 33 weeks.

Notes: Once lived in coastal rainforests, but has retreated to higher habitat. Good climber, with strong claws, short, broad feet. Tree-kangaroos are the only kangaroos able to walk rather than hop.

Status: Vulnerable.

Similar species: Bennett's Tree-kangaroo lacks pale head markings.

HABITAT
HIGHLAND RAINFORESTS

FOOD
LEAVES & FRUITS

42

Eastern Grey Kangaroo

Macropus giganteus (= gigantic great-foot)

Length: HB ♀ 96–186 ♂ 98–230 cm; T ♀ 45–84 ♂ 43–110 cm

Weight: ♀ up to 66 ♂ up to 32 kg

Identification: Large grey or grey-brown kangaroo with paler underparts. Unlike other kangaroos, has hair on muzzle between nostrils and upper lip.

Where found: Scrubland, woodland and forest from inland plains to eastern coastal Aust. and northeastern Tas.

Habits: Rests in the shade during day, then eats grasses from late afternoon to early morning. Males are larger than females and dominant males mate with most females. Joey carried in pouch 11 months, suckles another 9 months. Reserve embryo develops when pouch vacant.

Notes: Has increased using water and feed provided for cattle and sheep.

Status: Secure. Common.

Similar species: The Western Grey Kangaroo is browner than the Eastern Grey, and its range lies more to the west.

HABITAT SCRUBLANDS & WOODLANDS	FOOD GRASSES

Red Kangaroo

Macropus rufus (= red great-foot)

Length: HB ♀ 100 ♂ 115 cm;
T ♀ 82 ♂ 88 cm
Weight: ♀ 26.5 ♂ 66 kg
Identification: Very large

kangaroo (an exceptional male may weigh up to 85 kg). Red (male) or blue-grey or reddish (female) above, whitish below. Black and white patches at sides of muzzle, white stripe from mouth to ear. Naked area between nostril and lip.

Where found: Inland plains and woodlands, where water and green feed are available.

Habits: Rests during heat of day, feeds from dusk.

Notes: In drought, breeding activity in both males and females slows and pouch young may die. After rain, when green feed is available, breeding is successful. Each group led by a dominant male.

Status: Secure. Has probably increased in numbers since European settlement. Like Eastern Grey Kangaroo, when numbers build up may be harvested for meat and skins.

Similar species: None.

 HABITAT
INLAND
PLAINS

 **FOOD**
GRASSES

Common Wallaroo (Euro)

Macropus robustus (= strong great-foot)

Length: HB ♀ 134 ♂ 156 cm;
T: ♀ 64 ♂ 73 cm

Weight: ♀ 15.5 ♂ 26.5 kg

Identification: Large kangaroo usually found in rocky hill country. Dark grey or brown above, paler below. Fur coarse and sometimes shaggy. Area between nostril and lip is naked.

Where found: Drier areas of Aust., except for southwest and southeast. Not in Tas.

Habits: Solitary, on rocky hillslopes with grazing nearby. Shelters under ledges during day, eats grasses and shrubs at night. Can survive without drinking frequently.

Notes: Large male may be twice female weight. Called different names in east and west. Shaggy, dark grey Eastern Wallaroo lives on eastern and western slopes of Great Dividing Range. Shorter-haired, reddish Euro takes its

place across to the west coast.

Status: Secure. Common.

Similar species: Antilopine Wallaroo, more often seen on flatter country in far northern Australia, sometimes feeds with Euros near water.

HABITAT
ROCKY
HILL SLOPES

FOOD
GRASSES &
SHRUBS

45

Spectacled Flying-fox

Pteropus conspicillatus (= spectacled wing-foot)

Identification: Large megabat[G] with black body and wings, yellowish fur around eyes and down muzzle, neck ruff of yellow hair. Male ruff may be reddish from scented body fluid used in grooming.

Where found: Camps and feeds in or near rainforest in northeastern Qld.

Habits: Spends day in camp, flies out after dusk to feed on fruit, mainly in rainforest. One young one is carried by its mother while she feeds for 5 months.

Notes: Feeds on rainforest fruits. Carries fruit away to feed, or passes seeds through gut, so helps rainforest regeneration.

Status: Vulnerable. Disappears as rainforest cleared.

Similar species: Black and Grey-headed Flying-foxes lack very pale eye-rings.

Length: HB 22–24 cm

Weight: ♀ 500–650 g; ♂ 580–850 g

HABITAT
NE QLD
RAINFOREST

FOOD
RAINFOREST
FRUITS

Ghost Bat

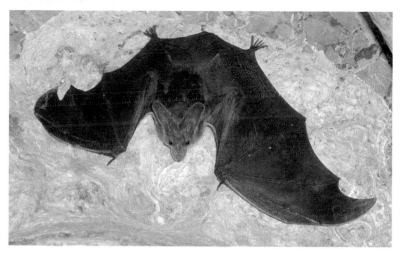

Macroderma gigas (= giant large-skin)

Length: HB 10–13 cm

Weight: 140–165 g

Identification: Large microbat[G] with large eyes, large ears joined at their bases and a simple noseleaf[G]. Fur grey above, paler below.

Where found: Groups survive in scattered locations across northern Aust. Roosts in caves, mine shafts, crevices.

Habits: At night swoops on small animals, including bats, holds them in its wings, bites and kills them, then carries them to a perch to be eaten. May use echolocation[G]. One young born Sept–Nov.

Notes: Has decreased in numbers in last 200 years.

Status: Rare and endangered.

Similar species: None.

HABITAT
ROOSTS
IN CAVES

FOOD
SMALL
ANIMALS

Bush Rat

Rattus fuscipes (= dusky-footed rat)

Length: HB 11–21 cm; T 10–19 cm

Weight: 40–225 g

Identification: Rat with pink, rounded ears and tail shorter than head and body.

Where found: In coastal forests, woodland and scrub with dense undergrowth in southwest, southeast and northeast Aust.

Habits: Prefers thick undergrowth. Eats grass-stems and leaves, fungi and insects.

Notes: Females are much smaller than males. Five young in a litter; are independent of their mother at 4–5 weeks. Only the season's young survive winter to breed in springtime. In High Country of southeastern NSW and northeastern Vic., lives in runways under snow in winter.

Status: Secure. Common in undisturbed habitat, but suffers when this is logged or burned. Repopulates after rain falls.

Similar species: Introduced Black Rat has longer tail and lives around human settlement.

JIRI LOCHMAN

HABITAT DENSE UNDERGROWTH

FOOD GRASS & FUNGI

Spinifex Hopping-mouse

Notomys alexis (= Alexandria Downs southern mouse)

Length: HB 10 cm; T 14 cm

Weight: 27–45 g

Identification: A rat-sized, hopping mouse, with large ears, long hindfeet and a very long, brush-tipped tail. Has a pouch under the throat. Pale brown above, white below.

Where found: Amongst spinifex on sand dunes and sandy flats in northwestern and central Aust.

Habits: Shelters from heat in below-ground nest chamber connected by shafts to surface. Eats seeds, roots and insects.

Notes: Hopping-mice use all four limbs when moving slowly, rise to hindlimbs to move at speed. 3–4 young are left in nest while female looks for food. Either female or male may retrieve a young one which wanders from the nest.

Status: Rare in dry conditions, breeds up after rainfall.

Similar species: Short-tailed Hopping Mouse (in the same habitat) is probably extinct.

M & I MORCOMBE

HABITAT ARID SAND COUNTRY

FOOD SEEDS & INSECTS

Western Pebble-mound Mouse

Pseudomys chapmani (= Chapman's false-mouse)

Length: HB 5.2–6.7 cm; T 7.3–7.9 cm

Weight: 10–15 g

Identification: Smaller than the House Mouse. Pale brown above, with paler paws; white below. Lives in burrows beneath mounds of small stones or pebbles.

Where found: Now, only in Pilbara area of WA. Old mounds show it was once found in the Gascoyne and Murchison River areas as well.

Habits: Piles stones, ranging up to 10 g in weight, into a mound above a burrow system containing nest chambers. A mound may cover 0.5–9m². It eats seeds and other vegetable material. Litter consists of 4 young.

Notes: First recorded in late 1970s. It may carry a pebble up to half its weight in its mouth, then position it with its forelimbs.

Status: Rare and disappearing.

Similar species: None in same area.

JIRI LOCHMAN

HABITAT
STONY
ARIDLANDS

FOOD
SEEDS &
PLANTS

Australian Sea-lion

Neophoca cinerea (= ash-coloured new-seal)

Length: HBT ♀ 160 ♂ 210 cm

Weight: ♀ 80 ♂ 300 kg

Identification: Seal with blunt snout and small rolled ears; on land, props itself upright on front flippers. Male dark with white crown and nape; female ash-grey above, cream below.

Where found: On offshore islands from the Abrolhos, WA, to Kangaroo Island, SA.

Habits: Swims using front flippers. Feeds at sea on squids and other marine creatures. Comes ashore on sandy beaches but breeds on rocky beaches, from Oct–Jan.

Notes: Only seal or sea-lion found exclusively in Aust. Hunted to near-extinction by sealers; absent from Bass Strait. Aggressive while breeding.

Status: Rare and vulnerable. There are only 3000–5000 Australian Sea-lions.

Similar species: Australian Fur-seal has dense underfur.

 HABITAT SEA & SEASHORE

FOOD MARINE ANIMALS

Bottlenosed Dolphin

Tursiops truncatus (= short-faced dolphin)

Length: 340–390 cm

Weight: 150–650 kg

Identification: Large, streamlined marine mammal with beaky snout, rounded forehead, backward-pointing dorsal[G] fin. Grey above, paler grey sides, off-white below.

Where found: In coastal or offshore waters anywhere around Aust. and Tas.

Habits: Usually in small groups. Often rides bow-waves of boats. Dives last up to 4 minutes, shows forehead but not beak when surfacing.

Notes: Eats fish, squid and other marine animals. Inquisitive and active; sometimes visits beaches.

Status: Probably secure.

Similar species: Dugong (p. 53).

 **HABITAT**
COASTS &
SEAS

 **FOOD**
FISH &
MARINE LIFE

Dugong

Dugong dugon (= Dugong)

Length: HBT ♀ 219
♂ 223 cm

Weight: 420 kg

Identification: Large, blunt-muzzled sea mammal with flippers and horizontal tail flukes⁶. Grey to brown above, paler below.

Where found: In shallow, calm, warm, sub-tropical and tropical coastal waters from Shark Bay, WA, around north of Aust. to Moreton Bay, Qld.

Habits: Lives in herds; feeds on seagrasses. Female breeds after reaching 9 years of age. Calf rides just above her back.

Notes: Dense bones keep it on the bottom while using broad upper lip to manipulate seagrasses into the mouth.

Status: Vulnerable to habitat alteration, hunting, netting.

Similar species: Bottlenosed Dolphin has a pointed snout, one blowhole on top of the head and a dorsal fin.

GEOFF TAYLOR

HABITAT
SHALLOW
SEAS

FOOD
SEA-
GRASSES

Humpback Whale

Megaptera novaeangliae (= New England great-wings)

Length: HBT 15 m

Weight: 25–45 tonnes

Identification: Large whale with massive head bearing callosities[G] on top and on lower jaw. 14–24 grooves on throat. Flippers are one-third as long as body. Hump in front of dorsal fin. Black above, mainly white below.

Where found: In winter, migrate from Antarctic waters up coasts of Australia to breed in warmer sub-tropical waters. Return in springtime.

Habits: Feeds on krill[G], filtered from Antarctic seas by baleen[G] in mouth. Does not feed while migrating. Males compete aggressively for right to mate with females.

Notes: Humpback Whales "sing" by shifting air around spaces in their bodies. All whales in an area sing the same song, which changes throughout the season.

Status: Since end of whaling, numbers have increased.

Similar species: Southern Right Whale has blunt-ended flippers, large, lumpy, white callosities on head.

HABITAT
SEAS

FOOD
KRILL

54

Dingo

Canis lupus (= dog-wolf)

Length: HB 86–122 cm;
T 26–38 cm

Weight: 9.6–24 kg

Identification: Medium-sized
dog, usually yellowish-ginger
but sometimes black-and-tan
or white. Usually white
markings on chest, tail tip
and paws. Pricked ears and
bushy tail.

Where found: All Aust.
except for Tas.

Habits: Lives in packs which
may meet at intervals or stay
together. Breed once a year.
Only dominant male and
female may breed, while others
help rear pups. Takes whatever
prey is common at the time,
from insects to large mammals
such as kangaroos.

Notes: Developed from Indian
Wolf around 6000 years ago.
Brought to Australia less than
4000 years ago by seafarers.
Hunting by humans does not
balance increase allowed
by bores, dams and rabbits.

Status: Secure. Common.

Similar species: Some breeds
of domestic dog. Hybrids
between Dingo and domestic
dog are increasing.

HABITAT
NEAR FOOD
& SHELTER

FOOD
ANIMALS,
ALL SIZES

Glossary ᴳ

anal. Of or near final opening of digestive tract.

baleen. In whales, fringed plates on upper jaw, used to strain sea water.

bask. Expose body to warmth.

callosities. Thick, hard skin areas.

canine. Pointed eyetooth of mammal.

carnivore. Animal which kills and eats other animals.

carrion. Dead flesh.

dominant. Controlling.

dorsal. On the back.

droppings. Digestive wastes. Faeces.

echolocation. Use of high-pitched sounds to locate objects.

embryo. Animal or plant in early stages of its development.

extinct. No longer in existence.

flukes. Flaps of a marine mammal's tail.

habitat. Where an animal or plant lives.

incubates. Keeps at a constant temperature.

introduced. Brought from another place or country.

joey. Young one of a kangaroo, wallaby or one of their relatives.

krill. Small crustaceans. Shrimps.

megabat. Large fruit-eating bat.

membrane. Sheet-like connective tissue, or thin, soft skin.

microbat. Small insect-eating bat.

native. Occurring naturally in that place or country.

noseleaf. Skin growth on muzzle of microbat, used in echo-location.

predator. Animal which kills to eat.

prehensile. Capable of grasping.

range. Geographical area in which an animal or plant occurs.

solitary. Living alone.

species. Group of similar animals which, mated, produce fertile offspring.

torpid. In a state of reduced activity due to cold.

venom. Poison of animal origin.

vulnerable. Exposed to injury.

weaning. Time of ceasing suckling.

Recommended further reading

CRONIN, L., 1991. *Key Guide to Australian Mammals*. Reed, Sydney.

SLATER, P. 2000. *Encyclopedia of Australian Wildlife*. Steve Parish Publishing, Brisbane.

SLATER, P., PARISH, S. 1997. *Amazing Facts About Australian Mammals*. Steve Parish Publishing, Brisbane.

STRAHAN, R. (Ed.) 1992. *Encyclopedia of Australian Animals: Mammals*. Angus & Robertson, Sydney.

STRAHAN, R. (Ed.) 1995. *The Mammals of Australia*. Reed Books, Sydney.

PHOTOGRAPHY: Steve Parish (uncredited) and Australia's finest nature photographers Jiri Lochman, Michael Morcombe, Stanley Breeden, Ian Morris, as credited.

ACKNOWLEDGEMENTS: The author's thanks are due to Leanne Nobilio whose design talent has contributed so much to this series. Audra Colless designed the cover and title page.

First published in Australia by Steve Parish Publishing Pty Ltd
PO Box 1058, Archerfield, Queensland 4108 Australia
www.steveparish.com.au
© copyright Steve Parish Publishing Pty Ltd, 1997
ISBN 1 74021 049 2

All rights reserved. No part of this publication may be reproduced, stored in a retrieval system, transmitted in any form by any means, electronic, mechanical, photocopying, recording or otherwise without the prior permission in writing of the publisher.